CITY *of* FIRE

Written by Alan Gibbons
Illustrated by Andrew Midgley

Collins Educational
An Imprint of HarperCollinsPublishers

I knew about it before the rest of the family. I was in my favourite place in the house, on the window ledge overlooking the narrow street. I used to sit there so I could chat to Mary. She lived opposite and we could reach out and touch, our windows were so close.

I smelt the smoke even before I saw the red glow over the rooftops. The air tasted bitter in my mouth and stung my eyes. The fire was not coming from one house, or even from one street of houses. It seemed as if the whole of London was ablaze.

"What's happening?" I called to Mary's father.
"The fire's coming our way. Tell everybody to
get out – quickly!"

I ran downstairs to tell my father, picking up my little brother James as I went.

"Father," I cried above the clatter of his printing press, "London's burning!" Father smiled.

"It isn't a joke," I cried, my voice trembling. "Look!"

When Father saw the smoke and the flames, he told us all to grab what we could and run. Once we were outside, I felt him squeeze my arm.

"Eliza," he said "you did well."

His words comforted me, and I felt a little less afraid.

We joined the crowds of frightened people, hurrying towards the River Thames. Some were screaming, most were just pressing forward in silence. "It's useless," said Father, as we passed firefighters with leather buckets and hoses battling against the flames.

Suddenly, buildings by the docks began to explode all around us. "Look out!" came a hoarse voice. A stream of flame was advancing on us.

"What is it?" cried James, staring at the blazing liquid.

"Brandy from the warehouses," my mother replied.

The fire was now a roaring giant, marching across the city.
It had already turned St. Paul's Cathedral into a bonfire.
The red-hot lead that had melted from the roof was
running through the streets.

We had to get away – across the river
where the fire could not reach us.
We hurried to the wharf where a ferryman
helped us into his boat.
"Will our house be burnt too?" I asked
Mother, thinking of my sunlit ledge
overlooking the street.
"I'm afraid so," she said. "It'll be a wonder
if there's anything left by tomorrow."
I clung closer to her and shut my eyes.

We slept that Monday night in the open air, listening to the roar of the fire. The next morning, we were woken by loud explosions from across the Thames. The Lord Mayor had ordered his men to blow up the houses in the fire's path.

The news came that evening that the fire had
stopped spreading.
"Thank God," said Father. "The plague last
year. Now this. Our London is a sad old place."

At last, in the late evening of the fourth day, the wind died down. The fire's roar was less fierce.

"At least it's nearly over," said Mother as we watched the glow on the river.

"If only it were," said Father. "Now we must begin to build the city over again."

We listened as he told us that thousands of homes had been burnt down, and that many of London's finest and most important buildings had been destroyed in the fire. But there was one building, more than any of these, that I would miss all my life – our little home above my father's print shop.

This story is about a real event, the Great Fire of London. In the early hours of the morning, on Sunday, September 2nd 1666, a fire began at John Farynor's bakery in Pudding Lane, a narrow street near London Bridge. All the nearby houses were built of wood and were so close together that the flames quickly spread. By dawn, dozens of houses were on fire. The king, Charles II, sent soldiers to help fight the fire, but it was already out of control. A strong east wind fanned the flames as they spread towards the River Thames, setting alight the warehouses in their path. The heat from the flames was so intense that, at times, the river water boiled.

After the fire had raged for three days, the Lord Mayor ordered soldiers to blow up houses in the fire's path to create a fire break. This was to starve the flames of fuel. On Wednesday, September 5th, the fire was eventually brought under control.

The cost of the fire was terrible. Although it had destroyed the plague, a disease which had ravaged the city before the fire, nine people had died and more than 100,000 people had lost their homes. They had to live in a great city of tents while their houses were rebuilt. Many of the new buildings were made of brick or stone as a precaution against fire. Some of London's finest buildings, including the Guildhall, the Bridewell and the Royal Exchange were destroyed. St. Paul's Cathedral was also razed to the ground, but was rebuilt by the architect Sir Christopher Wren. A monument to the Great Fire was built near Pudding Lane, as a reminder of the bravery shown by the people of London. It still stands to this very day.